LONGMAN CLASSICS

The

Sherlock
Holmes

Sir Arthur Conan Doyle

Simplified by Alan Pugh

Longman

Longman Group UK Limited,
Longman House, Burnt Mill, Harlow,
Essex CM20 2JE, England
and Associated Companies throughout the world.

First published 1987

ISBN 0-582-54155-7

Set in 10/13 point Linotron 202 Versailles
Produced by Longman Group (FE) Limited
Printed in Hong Kong

Acknowledgements

Photographs are from 'THE ADVENTURES OF SHERLOCK HOLMES,
COURTESY GRANADA TELEVISION' for pages 7, 11, 26, 43 and the
cover; TV Times/Transworld Feature Syndicate (UK) Ltd for
pages 30 and 39.

The cover background is a wallpaper design called NUAGE,
courtesy of Osborne and Little plc.

Stage 3: 1300 word vocabulary

Please look under *New words* at the back of this book
for explanations of words outside this stage.

Contents

Introduction

Sir Arthur Conan Doyle

Conan Doyle, born in 1859, was a doctor of medicine. He had a very keen mind, rather like that of his most famous character, Sherlock Holmes. His first story about Holmes, *A Study in Scarlet*, appeared in a magazine in 1887.

After 1890, Conan Doyel stopped practising medicine and became a full-time writer. More and more Sherlock Holmes stories appeared in magazines and were collected in books like *The Memoirs of Sherlock Holmes* (1894). Sherlock Holmes was also the subject of four full-length novels. The best-known of these is probably *The Hound of the Baskervilles* (1902), which has been made into films and television stories several times.

As a detective, Sherlock Holmes has unusual powers of reasoning and deduction. There are many examples in this book. In *The Six Napoleons* Holmes deduces that it is the busts that are important. In *The Norwood Builder* he deduces Oldacre's hiding place when he finds one passage shorter than the others. In *The Golden Glasses* he makes many deductions, including the ones he makes from the glasses themselves.

Holmes's friend, Doctor Watson, is not a fool (though some films have made him seem foolish), but he is an ordinary man without Holmes's special powers of mind. He is a brave man, and is often able to help the detective in moments of danger. In very many of Holmes's cases, Watson tells us the story, and so we receive the explanations that Watson himself needs.

Holmes's great enemy in a number of his cases was the master criminal Moriarty. When Conan Doyle· decided that he had written enough Sherlock Holmes stories, he wrote one in which Moriarty killed the great detective. There was a public outcry. Doyle's readers were quite angry, and he had to write a story in which Holmes appeared again – he hadn't died, after all! This was the first story of a collection called *The Return of Sherlock Holmes* (1904). The three stories in this book come from that collection.

Although the world remembers Conan Doyle as the writer of Sherlock Holmes stories, he himself wanted to be remembered for his more "serious" writing. This writing included some historical novels, for example, *The White Company* (1890), *Rodney Stone* (1896), and *Sir Nigel* (1906).

Modern detective stories usually deal with murder. Although there are murders in two of the stories in this book, and a pretended murder in the third, Sherlock Holmes's cases do not necessarily include murder. In some cases there is not even a crime, because Sherlock Holmes has prevented the crime. The character of the detective and the way his mind works (his methods) are important in the Sherlock Holmes stories. What Conan Doyle never forgot – and what some modern writers do forget – was that the story is also important, and that the reader must feel that he or she is present as the story unfolds.

A note from Dr Watson

Sherlock Holmes was one of the cleverest and most important detectives in all England some years ago. The police often asked him to help them. My name is Dr Watson, and I helped Holmes with many of his cases.

In 1891, Holmes and I had to go away from England on a case. While we were away Holmes disappeared. Everyone thought he had been killed. I was very sad; I was sure my friend was dead.

Then, one day in 1894, Holmes returned to England. He was not dead! I was very happy to see him again. Soon we began to work on cases once more. Holmes was now an even better detective than he had been before.

This little book is called *The Return of Sherlock Holmes* because the stories in it come from the collection of stories with that name. In it I wrote about the cases we worked on after Holmes's return. Here, I want to tell you about three of the best cases from this time: *The Six Napoleons, The Norwood Builder* and *The Golden Glasses*. I hope you will enjoy reading them.

Dr Watson

The Six Napoleons

Chapter 1

Mr Lestrade, a detective from Scotland Yard, often visited my friend Sherlock Holmes and me in the evening. Holmes enjoyed talking to Lestrade because he learned useful facts about what was happening at London's most important police station. Lestrade liked these visits too, because Holmes was a good detective and always listened carefully if Lestrade had a difficult case. Holmes could often help Lestrade.

On one of these evening visits Lestrade talked only about the weather and other uninteresting things for a long time. After that, he stopped talking and sat quietly thinking. Holmes was interested in his silence.

"Have you got a good case for me today?" he asked.

"Oh, it's nothing very important, Mr Holmes," the detective answered.

Sherlock Holmes laughed. "Please tell me all about it," he said.

"Well, Mr Holmes, there is something, but it doesn't seem very important and I don't want to trouble you with it. I know you like difficult things, but I think this may interest Dr Watson more than you."

I was surprised when Lestrade said this. I am a doctor, not a real detective, so I said, "What's the matter? Is somebody ill?"

"Yes, I think so. I think somebody is very ill," was Lestrade's answer. "I think he must be completely mad!"

He then told us that someone had been taking plaster busts of Napoleon Bonaparte and breaking them.

"Four days ago he went into a shop in Kennington Road. The owner's name is Morse Hudson and he sells works of art," said Lestrade. "You know, paintings and such things. When nobody was looking the madman took a bust of Napoleon and broke it. Then he ran away. He must hate Napoleon very much."

"Why are you so interested in this?" said Holmes.

"Because he's done it again," replied Lestrade. "Yesterday, he got into the house of a doctor. The doctor, his name is Doctor Barnicott, is very interested in Napoleon, and he had bought two busts from Morse Hudson's shop. He kept one bust at home and the other in the house where he worked near the centre of London. The thief took the bust from his home and broke it against the garden wall. Dr Barnicott found it when he got up in the morning. He went to his place of work at about twelve o'clock and he was very surprised to find that the second bust had been broken too."

"This is more interesting," said Holmes. "Did the thief break anything else, or take anything?"

"No, he didn't."

"And these three busts were exactly the same?"

"Yes, they were."

"Well," said Holmes, "the thief may be interested only in these busts and not in Napoleon himself."

"That is possible," Lestrade replied. "But there can't be many busts of Napoleon in this part of London, so we can't be very sure."

"What do you think about all this?" I asked Lestrade.

"I don't know, Doctor Watson," he replied. "I don't know what to think."

Chapter 2

Next morning I was dressing when Holmes came into my room. "Lestrade wants to see us as soon as possible," he said. "He's at a house in Kensington."

I quickly finished dressing and we had a cup of coffee, then we went to Kensington.

The house was in a quiet street, but it was not far from the busy centre of London. That morning there was a large crowd of people standing outside.

Lestrade was waiting for us. He was looking very serious. I noticed that there was a lot of blood outside the front door of the house. Lestrade told us to come inside and we met the man who lived there. His name was Horace Harker and he worked for a newspaper, but today he was too troubled to write anything about what had just happened.

"Please tell us what you know, Mr Harker," said Lestrade.

Mr Harker's voice sounded very frightened. He said, "About four months ago I bought a bust of Napoleon from Harding Brothers' shop in the High Street. I was woken by a loud cry at about three o'clock this morning. I was very frightened, but I went down to see who was there. There was nobody in the room, but the window was open and I saw that the bust of Napoleon had gone. I opened the front door to call a policeman and I found a dead man lying there. He was covered in blood – I felt very sick."

"Who is the dead man?" asked Holmes.

"We don't know," Lestrade answered. "The only things he had with him were a cheap street map of London and a photograph of a very ugly man. There was a small knife beside him, but I don't know if it killed him."

"What about the bust of Napoleon?" asked Holmes.

"It was found quite near here in the garden of an empty house. It had been broken just like the others," said Lestrade.

Holmes, Lestrade and I went to look at the broken bust. Mr Harker stayed at home. He wanted to write something about the case for his newspaper now because he was beginning to feel a little better and it was a good story.

Chapter 3

We soon arrived at the empty house. The pieces of the bust were lying in the grass by the garden wall. Holmes picked up some of the pieces and looked at them carefully.

"Well?" said Lestrade.

Holmes looked at him. "There is a lot more work for us to do," he said. "But there are some interesting questions here for us to think about. For example, why was a man not afraid to kill someone to get a cheap bust like this? Another thing, if he only wanted to break the bust, why didn't he break it at Mr Harker's house? Why did he take it away with him?"

"I expect he carried it away because he was afraid of being caught by Mr Harker," said Lestrade.

"That may be the reason," said Holmes. "But why did he bring it to this house and not another one?"

"Because this house was empty," replied Lestrade.

"But there is another empty house in this road nearer to Mr Harker's house. Why didn't he break it there?"

"I really don't know," replied Lestrade.

Holmes pointed to the street light above our heads. "Because he could see what he was doing here; the garden of the other house was too dark."

"Good Heavens! That's true," said the detective. Then he asked, "But how does this help us, Mr Holmes?"

"I don't know yet," my friend answered. "But I shall remember it. What are you going to do next, Mr Lestrade?"

"I want to find out who the dead man was, then I can find out why he was in Kensington last night and who met and killed him outside Mr Harker's house. Isn't that a good idea?"

"Possibly," replied Sherlock Holmes. "But it isn't my way."

"What do you want to do?" asked Lestrade.

"I will do things in my way and you can do things in your way," Holmes said. "Then we can talk about the case together later."

Then Holmes said something surprising. "If you see Mr Harker, please tell him that I am sure that a dangerous madman who hates Napoleon was in his house last night."

Lestrade was surprised, "Do you really think that's true?"

Holmes laughed. "Not really," he said, "but I think that the readers of Mr Harker's newspaper will be interested. We must go now, but please visit us in our rooms in Baker Street at six o'clock this evening. Please may I keep the photograph which the dead man had with him until then? When you come to Baker Street, you must be ready to go out somewhere with me. Until then goodbye and good luck!"

Chapter 4

Sherlock Holmes and I walked together to the High Street. We stopped at the shop of Harding Brothers. Mr Harding was not there and Holmes was not pleased by this. He decided instead to visit Morse Hudson's shop where Dr Barnicott had bought his busts.

Morse Hudson was very angry about the broken busts, but he answered all Holmes's questions. He told us that he had bought some busts from the place where they were made, Gelder and Company, in another part of London. He said that he couldn't help us very much, but when Holmes showed him the photograph he cried, "That's Beppo!"

"Who is Beppo?" asked Holmes.

"He's an Italian. He used to work here in my shop, but he left last week. I don't know where he went. He left two days before the bust was broken. Perhaps he broke it."

We thanked Morse Hudson and left his shop. Holmes was quite pleased with what the shopkeeper had told us. He decided next to visit Gelder and Company, the place where the busts were made.

We passed through many parts of London, rich places and poor places, before we came to Stepney. Stepney was once a rich place but now the people who lived there were poor working people; many of them came from other countries.

We soon found Gelder and Company. The man who spoke to us was a German. He told us that they had made hundreds of busts in the past, but this year they had made only six. Three had been sold to Morse Hudson and three to Harding. He told us that the busts were cheaply made, usually by Italian workers. When Holmes showed him the photograph of the ugly Italian he became angry.

"That is a very bad man," he said. "His name is Beppo and he used to work here for me. That was more than a year ago."

"Why did he leave?" Holmes asked.

"He tried to kill another Italian with a knife in the street," replied the German. "The police followed him here

Sherlock Holmes and Dr Watson outside their Baker Street address

and caught him. Because the other Italian didn't die, Beppo was sent to prison for only one year. One of his friends works here now. Do you want to speak to him?"

"No, no!" said Holmes. "Please don't tell him anything – this is very important."

"All right," said the man.

"I have one more question," said Holmes. "I noticed in your book that you sold the busts on 3rd June last year. Can you tell me when the police arrested Beppo?"

"Yes, I can. I last paid Beppo on 20th May last year, so it must have been very soon after that."

"You have helped me a lot," said Holmes. "I must go now. Remember, don't say anything to Beppo's friend."

It was late in the afternoon and we were hungry, so we had some food in a restaurant before doing anything else. Holmes bought a newspaper to read. In it Mr Harker had written an exciting story about the madman who hated Napoleon. Most of the story was not true, but Holmes laughed a lot; he thought it was a good joke.

"It is easy to make these people help us, Watson," he said.

I didn't really understand what he meant, but I laughed too at the silly story.

When we had finished our meal, we went to Harding Brothers. Mr Harding was a busy little man and he answered our questions quickly and clearly. He had sold one bust to Mr Harker, the one that had been broken. He had sold one to a Mr Josiah Brown, of Chiswick, London. The other one had been bought by someone from outside London: Mr Sandeford of Reading.

Holmes seemed very interested in these facts and thanked Mr Harding. It was late, so we hurried back to Baker Street to meet Lestrade.

Chapter 5

Lestrade was waiting for us when we arrived. He was very pleased with himself.

"Have you found out anything important, Mr Holmes?" he asked.

"Well, we know a lot about the busts now," Holmes replied.

"The busts!" said Lestrade, and laughed. "I know you are a clever detective, Mr Holmes, but I think I have found out something more important than that!"

"What have you found out?"

"I now know who the dead man was and I think I have found the reason why he was killed," was Lestrade's reply.

"Very good, Mr Lestrade." Holmes smiled and waited.

Lestrade continued. "We have a detective at Scotland Yard who knows many of the Italians living in London. He knew this man very well. His name was Pietro Venucci; he was a thief and a very dangerous man. He was a member of the Mafia, the Italian secret society. It was his job, I think, to punish others in the society if they broke the rules – usually by killing them. The man in the photograph must have broken the rules and Venucci was following him. They had a fight and Venucci was killed."

Holmes smiled at Lestrade and said, "Very good, Mr Lestrade; you have told me why the busts were broken very clearly."

Lestrade nearly shouted at Holmes, "Those busts! Can't you forget them, Mr Holmes? They are not important; a man will only go to prison for six months for breaking them. Pietro Venucci is dead, that's what interests me."

"I see," said Holmes quietly. "What are you going to do next, Mr Lestrade?"

"I'm going to go to the part of London where the

9

Italians live. I want to find the man in the photograph. Do you want to come with me?"

Holmes did not seem very interested. "No, thank you. I think we can find him much more easily in another place tonight."

"Really! Where?"

"At an address in Chiswick. If you come with me tonight I will go anywhere you like tomorrow," said Holmes.

Lestrade was surprised, but he agreed. All three of us had an early dinner together, then Holmes told Lestrade and me to rest until eleven o'clock.

Holmes did not rest. He spent the time in his room looking at some of the many old newspapers that he kept there. I thought that he was probably looking for some facts about Venucci or Beppo.

Chapter 6

Lestrade and I woke up at half past ten. Holmes was waiting for us. He told me to bring my gun and I saw him pick up his favourite strong walking stick before we left the house.

We quickly drove to Chiswick, and Holmes took us to a large house in a dark street. I thought that the people inside must have already gone to bed because the house was so dark and quiet.

"I'm glad it's not raining," said Holmes quietly. "We may have to wait a long time. We mustn't smoke and we must be very quiet, but I hope we are going to discover something tonight."

We waited for five minutes but we didn't have to wait much longer. The garden gate suddenly opened and a man ran quickly down the garden path towards the house.

10

Holmes and Watson wait in the dark outside the house in Chiswick

It was so dark and he moved so quickly that it was impossible to see his face. He disappeared into the darkness and we waited in silence.

The next thing we heard was the sound of a window opening very slowly, then we saw a small light inside the front room of the house.

"Let's go to the open window, then we can catch him as he comes out," said Lestrade.

But before we could move, the man had come outside again. In the light we could see that he had something white under his arm. He looked round to see if anyone was watching him, then there was a sudden crash as he broke the thing against the wall. He was so busy that he didn't see the three of us coming towards him. Holmes jumped on his back and he fell to the ground heavily. Lestrade and I quickly ran to help Holmes; I had my gun ready and soon it was impossible for the man to escape.

He looked up at us. His face was very ugly and we could see that he was surprised and angry. Immediately I saw that it was the man in the photograph.

While we were holding the man on the ground, Holmes was looking at the pieces of another bust of Napoleon, which the man had broken against the wall. He lifted up each piece and looked at it in the light. He was just finishing when somebody turned on the lights in the house. Next a short fat man wearing a shirt and trousers came up to Holmes; he was smiling.

"You must be Mr Sherlock Holmes?" he said.

"That is correct," said Holmes. "And you must be Mr Josiah Brown."

"Yes, sir. We did everything you told us. We locked all the doors inside the house and turned off all the lights. Then we waited very quietly. You have done very well –

please come inside and have something to eat and drink."

Holmes thanked Mr Brown, but Lestrade wanted to take the man away, so we all drove to Scotland Yard. The thief said nothing all the way but he looked at us all the time. His ugly white face was like an animal's. When we arrived at Scotland Yard, Holmes and I stayed long enough to discover that the man had nothing with him except a long knife, with dry blood on it, and a little money.

As we were going, Lestrade said, "Well, Mr Holmes, I must thank you for all your help. I think you will agree now that all my ideas were correct."

Holmes smiled and said, "It's rather late now for me to explain, but I think you will find that the business of the busts is much more important than you think. Can you come to see me again at six o'clock tomorrow evening?"

"Of course," said Lestrade. "I'm always happy to visit you. I shall be pleased to come."

As we were going home, Holmes said to me, "I think Lestrade is a good detective, but he doesn't understand everything about this case. I think that this is one of the most unusual cases I have ever worked on, Watson."

"Really?" I said, "What else is there to explain, Holmes?"

"The busts, Watson. I think they are the most important part of this case."

Chapter 7

At six o'clock next evening Lestrade came to Baker Street to see us. He had found out many things about Beppo. He was a well-known thief and he had killed a number of people. He was also very good at making busts and other works of art. He had been living in London for years and could speak good English – when he wanted to.

It was possible that he had made the busts at Gelder and Company's shop. Holmes listened to everything that Lestrade said with a smile on his face, but I could see that he was really thinking about something else. He already knew all the things that Lestrade was saying and he was waiting to tell him something he didn't know; something very surprising, I was sure.

The doorbell rang and we heard someone coming towards the door of the room where we were sitting. An old man came in. He had a red face and he was carrying a large bag. He put the bag on the table.

"Is Mr Sherlock Holmes here?" he asked.

Holmes smiled and said, "I am Sherlock Holmes and you must be Mr Sandeford of Reading. I'm pleased to meet you. This is my friend Dr Watson and this is Mr Lestrade from Scotland Yard."

We both said hello to Mr Sandeford. He told Holmes that he had the bust of Napoleon for him. He also had a letter from Holmes. He said to Lestrade and me, "Gentlemen, I want you to hear what Mr Holmes says in this letter. He sent it to me yesterday." He read it to us.

Dear Mr Sandeford,

Mr Harding, of Harding Brothers, the art shop, has told me that you bought the last plaster bust of Napoleon he had. I want that bust very much and I will pay ten pounds for it. Please bring it to my rooms in Baker Street, London, tomorrow at half-past six.

Yours faithfully,
Sherlock Holmes.

Then he said to Holmes, "Do you know how much I paid for the bust in this bag?"

"No, I don't," said Holmes.

"Well, I'm not a thief, Mr Holmes. I want you to know that I only paid fifteen shillings for it. If you don't want to buy it now that you know its true price, I shall be quite happy."

"No," said Holmes. "I still want the bust. Here is ten pounds." He gave the money to Mr Sandeford.

"Thank you very much," said Mr Sandeford. He took the money and opened the bag. Inside was an ordinary plaster bust of Napoleon just like the others.

Holmes said, "Thank you, Mr Sandeford. Now, before you go, I want you to write your name on this piece of paper. It says that you have sold the bust to me for ten pounds and it is mine now."

"Of course," said Mr Sandeford. He wrote his name on the paper and left.

Chapter 8

As soon as Mr Sandeford had gone, Holmes started to do strange things. Lestrade and I watched him carefully. First he took a clean white cloth from the cupboard and laid it on the table. Next he carefully put the bust on the cloth. He took his stick and hit the bust hard. It broke into small pieces. Holmes shouted loudly and picked up a small black thing from the cloth. Lestrade and I were silent.

"This is the Black Pearl of the Borgias!" said Holmes.

We were both very surprised. "Well done, Holmes!" I cried. "How did you know it was there?"

"It's impossible," said Lestrade quietly.

Holmes explained. He told us that this, the most well-known pearl in the world, had been stolen from the hotel room of the Princess of Colonna on 22nd May the year before. "I'm sure you remember that, Mr Lestrade," said Holmes.

"Yes, I do," replied Lestrade.

"Well," Holmes continued, "you may also remember that the hotel where she was staying was near to the part of London where Gelder and Company have their shop. The police thought that the pearl might have been taken by an Italian girl who worked at the hotel. Her name was Lucretia Venucci and I think that the man who was killed two nights ago was her brother Pietro.

"I looked at my old newspapers and discovered that Beppo was taken to prison only two days after the pearl was stolen. This was the same time that the busts were being made. I think that Pietro Venucci and Beppo worked together to steal the pearl. Perhaps Venucci stole it, then Beppo stole it from him; it doesn't matter.

"The important thing is that Beppo had the pearl with him when the police tried to catch him after the street fight he had with another Italian. He ran to Gelder's and wanted to hide the pearl – but where? He didn't have much time and he saw the soft plaster busts of Napoleon which had just been made and were not yet dry. He pushed the pearl into one of them and covered the hole. He could do this quickly and easily because he had made many busts like it in the past. It was the perfect place to hide the pearl.

"Because of the fight, Beppo was sent to prison for one year. During that time the six busts were sold but, luckily for Beppo, he had a friend who worked at Gelder's. I think this friend was able to tell him who bought the busts.

"There were only six busts, five in London and one in Reading. Beppo started looking for the one with the pearl in it. Of course it was best for him to begin in London. Venucci knew that Beppo knew where the pearl was. When Beppo came out of prison, Venucci tried to find him. At last he followed Beppo to Mr Harker's house in Kensington. They fought, and Beppo killed Venucci."

"If Venucci knew Beppo well, why did he carry his photograph?" asked Lestrade.

"To ask other people if they had seen Beppo, when he was trying to find him," replied Holmes. "Of course I couldn't be sure that the pearl had not been in Mr Harker's bust but I warned Josiah Brown and his family. We were lucky; the pearl was not in Mr Harker's bust. Beppo went to Mr Brown's house and we caught him. I knew then that the pearl must be in Mr Sandeford's bust.

"What Mr Harker wrote in the newspaper helped us. He made Beppo think that the police had the wrong idea. He thought that they were looking for a madman who hated Napoleon; he didn't know that I had discovered the true secret of the busts. Now we have the pearl and the man who killed Venucci."

"Mr Holmes," said Lestrade, "I have seen you work on many cases in the past, but this is one of the best. My friends at Scotland Yard will, I am sure, be very interested in the case and the way you have worked on it. Can you come and meet them tomorrow? If you can, I am sure they will be very pleased to talk to you."

"I shall be happy to come," said Holmes. "Thank you."

"It is *I* that must thank *you*," said Lestrade. "I didn't understand this case completely. Without your help I am sure I would never have found the pearl."

Holmes smiled for a moment. I think he didn't quite know what to say. Then suddenly his face changed.

"Well, Watson," he said, "we have work to do. This is not our only case! Goodbye, Lestrade. If you have any more little cases for me I shall be happy to help you with them, if I can."

The Norwood Builder

Chapter 1

"There seem to be no interesting cases any more, Watson,"
Sherlock Holmes said to me. "London isn't interesting
now."

"I don't think the people of London would say that," I
answered.

"Well, I suppose I mustn't think only of myself," he said.
He smiled as he pushed his chair back from the breakfast
table. "It is better for everybody if detectives like me have
nothing to do."

I smiled too. Holmes had really had quite a lot of work
during the past few months. But I must say that the world
seemed very quiet that morning.

Sherlock Holmes sat back in his chair. He picked up his
newspaper. He was just going to start reading when there
was a loud ring on the doorbell. I heard Mrs Hudson open
the door (she was the lady who cooked and cleaned for us).
Somebody ran into the house very quickly. He opened our
door and stood in front of us. He looked very frightened
and I thought he had been running, because he was
breathing hard.

He suddenly seemed to remember that Holmes and I
must be surprised to see him come in like that.

"I'm sorry, Mr Holmes," he cried. "I must talk to you
now. I can't wait. I feel very frightened. I am John Hector
McFarlane; you must know my name already."

"Sit down, Mr McFarlane," said Holmes. "No, I don't

know your name. I can see that you're not married and that you're a lawyer."

The man seemed surprised that Holmes knew these things, but it didn't surprise me. Holmes was a good detective, and he had noticed the man's untidy clothes and the lawyers' papers in his hand.

"Yes, that is true, Mr Holmes," he replied. "And it is also true that I am the unhappiest man in London today. You must help me! The police are coming to arrest me. A detective followed me from the station to your house. I don't mind going with them if you will help me."

"The police are coming?" said Holmes. He looked very happy. I knew that he hoped there was going to be an interesting case for him. Then he remembered poor Mr McFarlane and said, "I'm sorry, Mr McFarlane; I wasn't thinking about you. This sounds very interesting. Why do the police want you?"

"They think I killed a man called Jonas Oldacre, who lived at Lower Norwood."

Our visitor picked up the newspaper and I could see that his hands were shaking. Holmes had not started reading it yet.

"If you look at your newspaper, you will see why I have come to see you, Mr Holmes," he said. "I think everyone in London must know my name by now. Look here in the middle pages."

FIRE AT LOWER NORWOOD. RICH MAN DISAPPEARS. IS HE DEAD? HAS HE BEEN KILLED?

"It says here that the police think I may have killed Mr Oldacre for his money. It will make my poor old mother very unhappy. What can I do?"

I looked at Mr McFarlane carefully. He was a hand-

19

some man with fair hair. I thought he was about twenty-seven years old and his good clothes showed me that he had plenty of money.

Holmes said, "There isn't much time, Watson. Please read what it says in the newspaper." This is what I read.

Late last night, or early this morning, something happened at Lower Norwood and the police are afraid that an important man may be dead. Everybody in Lower Norwood knows the name of Mr Jonas Oldacre the builder. He is sixty-two years old, and is not married. He lives at Deep Dene house in Sydenham Road. He has few friends and doesn't like meeting people. He made a lot of money as a builder when he was a young man but he doesn't work any more. He still keeps a lot of wood at the back of his house. Last night, at about twelve o'clock, a lot of that wood caught fire – or someone set fire to it. It was impossible to stop it burning. At first, it seemed like an ordinary fire, but then someone noticed that the owner of the house was not there. They found that he had not slept in his bed. In one room there were some important papers on the table and it looked as if someone had been fighting there. A stick was found on the floor and also a little blood. The police know that Mr Oldacre had a visitor last night and they think the stick belongs to him. He is a lawyer and his name is Hector McFarlane.

At the bottom of the page were some more facts which had been added later.

Some people are already saying that Mr McFarlane has been arrested. If he has not, the police are certainly

20

looking for him. At Norwood, it seems that something heavy was pulled through the grass from the house to the place where the wood was. They say it is possible that a dead body was burned with the wood. They seem to think that Mr Oldacre was killed in his house then taken outside and burned. Mr Lestrade, of Scotland Yard, is working on the case and we are sure that he will soon say what happened.

The first thing Sherlock Holmes asked Mr McFarlane was why the police had not already arrested him.

"I live with my mother and father at Torrington Lodge, Blackheath," said Mr McFarlane. "But last night I was not at home. I stayed at a hotel near Mr Oldacre's house in Norwood because I had visited him very late in the evening. The police will try to catch me at home or at my office this morning, or a detective may even come here for me."

Chapter 2

Suddenly our doorbell rang again and we heard Mrs Hudson letting some men in. The door opened and our friend Lestrade, the detective from Scotland Yard, came in. Lestrade looked at McFarlane and said, "You are John Hector McFarlane and you must come with me because you killed Jonas Oldacre last night."

McFarlane stood up; his face was white.

"Sit down," said Holmes. "And Mr Lestrade, please sit down too."

"But I must take Mr McFarlane away," said Lestrade.

"Half an hour doesn't matter to you," replied Holmes. "And Mr McFarlane was just going to tell us what happened last night."

"Well, Mr Holmes," said Lestrade. "Because you are my friend and you have helped me in the past, I will wait for half an hour, no more than that."

"Thank you," said Holmes. Then he asked Mr McFarlane to tell us exactly what had happened.

Mr McFarlane began. "Yesterday morning I knew nothing about Mr Oldacre except his name. He used to be a friend of my mother and father but he is not any more. I was very surprised when he came to my office yesterday. He had these pieces of paper with him and he said that his will was written on them. I am a lawyer and he said that he wanted me to make a proper copy of it for him. He wanted to wait while I wrote it. I began the work and I soon saw that he wanted *me* to have all his money when he was dead. I couldn't understand why, so I asked him. He told me that as he had no children of his own he wanted me to have the money because he used to know my father.

"Of course I thanked him for his great kindness, but I was still very surprised. I made the copy as quickly as possible. When I had finished he asked me to go to his house that night to see some more important papers. The last thing he said was, 'Please don't tell your mother and father. I want this to be a surprise for them.'

"Well, Mr Holmes," McFarlane continued, "he had been so kind to me that I wanted to do exactly what he said. I told my father that I had important business and might be very late home from work.

"Mr Oldacre asked me to come to him at nine o'clock but it took me a long time to find his house and I didn't arrive until half past nine. When I saw Mr Oldacre——"

"Stop!" said Sherlock Holmes. "Who opened the door for you?"

"An old woman. I think she worked for Mr Oldacre,"

replied Mr McFarlane.

"And was it she who told Mr Oldacre that you had arrived?" asked Holmes.

"Yes, it was," he replied. "Then she took me into a room where there was a simple meal waiting for me on the table. I ate some of the food, then Mr Oldacre took me to his bedroom. There was a strong cupboard in the room and he took a lot of papers from it. We worked on them for a long time and didn't finish until about half past eleven. Mr Oldacre told me I had better leave quietly by the back door because the old woman was asleep.

"When I was leaving I couldn't find my stick, but Mr Oldacre said, 'That doesn't matter, my boy. You can collect it another day. I hope you are going to visit me very often from now on.'

"When I left him, the cupboard was open and the papers were on the table. It was too late to go back to Blackheath, so I stayed at the Anerly Arms in Norwood. I didn't know about all ·this until I read the paper this morning."

Mr McFarlane stopped speaking and Lestrade said, "Have you any more questions, Mr Holmes?"

"No. I want to go to Blackheath first," said Holmes.

"Don't you mean Norwood?" asked Lestrade.

"Perhaps ..." replied Holmes and he smiled at Lestrade. The detective looked as if he didn't understand. Holmes often understood things more quickly than Lestrade did and the detective knew this.

Lestrade said, "There are two policemen waiting for you outside, Mr McFarlane. You must go with them now."

The policemen took Mr McFarlane away. His face was still white and he looked at Holmes very sadly, but he said nothing.

Chapter 3

Lestrade stayed in the room with us after McFarlane had gone. Holmes picked up the papers that the lawyer had left. He looked at them, then gave them to Lestrade.

"These are very interesting, aren't they, Lestrade?" he said.

Lestrade looked at the papers for a minute then said, "I can understand the first few lines perfectly, the writing is good. After that the writing is so bad that I can't read it. Later on, there are a few more good lines, then the writing is bad again."

"Why do you think it is like that?" asked Holmes.

"Why do *you* think it is like that?" replied Lestrade.

"The answer is very simple," said Holmes. "Mr Oldacre wrote this on the train when he was coming to London to see Mr McFarlane. The good parts were written at stations, the bad parts were written when the train was moving."

Lestrade laughed and said, "Very good, Mr Holmes. But how does that help us with the case?"

"Well," said Holmes. "I think it is rather surprising that a man should write his will on the train; it seems as if he didn't think it was really going to be very important."

"It was very important for him," said Lestrade. "It is because of his will that he is dead now."

"Do you think that's true?" asked Holmes.

"Don't you?" replied Lestrade.

"It's possible, but the case is not very clear to me yet," was Holmes's answer.

"Not clear?" said Lestrade. "It's very clear to me. When McFarlane knew that he would get Mr Oldacre's money, he went to Norwood and killed him. Then he burned the dead body with the wood. He hoped that nobody would know what had happened to Mr Oldacre because they would find nothing. It seems very simple to me."

"Too simple," said Holmes. "McFarlane is not a fool and it would be very foolish to kill a man on exactly the same day that he had made his will. It would also be silly to kill Mr Oldacre when his servant knew who was in the house. Remember the old woman let Mr McFarlane in. Another thing, why should he burn the body so carefully, but be careless and leave his stick behind in the room?"

"You know very well, Mr Holmes," said Lestrade, "that when a man has just killed someone he doesn't always think very clearly. It is easy to forget a thing like a stick. Perhaps he was afraid to go back to the room. Can you give me any other reason why Mr Oldacre was killed?"

"I can think of many possible reasons," said Holmes. "For example, suppose a man was passing the house and saw the two men in the room with the papers. He might think that they had money there. When Mr McFarlane left, this man could come in through the window and kill Mr Oldacre."

"Why didn't he take anything?" asked Lestrade.

"Because he found only papers; there was no money in the room," said Holmes.

Lestrade did not seem very sure of his ideas any more but he said, "Well, you may look for your man if you want to, Mr Holmes, but I think it was McFarlane who killed Mr Oldacre. He had a perfect reason and was also the only person in the world who did not need to take anything because everything was going to be his soon."

"I didn't say that you were wrong," replied Sherlock Holmes. "I only wanted to show you that there were other possible ways in which Mr Oldacre was killed. Goodbye,

Mr McFarlane and Mr Oldacre with the important papers

Mr Lestrade. I expect I shall come to see you at Norwood later today."

Lestrade left us and Holmes started to put on his coat.

"I'm going to Blackheath," he said.

"Why not Norwood?" I asked.

"Two strange things have happened, my friend, and the police are only thinking about one of them. The first thing was the strange will. I want to know why Oldacre wanted to give his money to Mr McFarlane."

"Do you want me to come with you?" I asked.

"No, it isn't necessary; you can't help me. There is no danger at Blackheath," replied Holmes.

Chapter 4

It was quite late when my friend returned from Blackheath and I could see that he was not happy. He said, "I am afraid the case is difficult, Watson. This time I think that Lestrade may be right. I still don't think McFarlane killed Oldacre, but the facts help Lestrade and they don't help me. I'm afraid he will win."

"Did you go to Blackheath?" I asked.

"Yes, I did," said Holmes, "and I quickly found out that Oldacre was a very nasty man indeed. I spoke to Mr McFarlane's mother. She was very angry and afraid. She told me that many years ago Oldacre wanted to marry her. She would not become his wife because she discovered that he had been very cruel to some animals he had. This made him angry. On the day of Mrs McFarlane's marriage to her present husband he sent her a copy of her photograph which he had cut into small pieces. He also sent a letter saying that he hated her and her new husband. If the police discover this they will think that young Mr McFarlane had another reason for killing Oldacre.

"I discovered nothing else at Blackheath, so I went to Norwood."

Holmes showed me a plan he had made of Oldacre's house and garden. The garden was large and the place where the wood was kept was a long way from the nearest road. Lestrade had not been there when Holmes visited the house but another policeman had shown him everything.

"They have found some pieces of Oldacre's clothes where the fire was," continued Holmes, "and a doctor has told them that it is possible that a man or an animal was burned there. I looked at everything very carefully, but I found nothing new. There is very little blood in the bedroom and there are the marks of only two men's feet on the floor.

"I found that Oldacre had not got as much money at the bank as people said he had. I don't think that killing him would make McFarlane a rich man.

"Then I spoke to the old woman, Oldacre's servant. I think she knows something but she wouldn't tell me very much. She told me she had let McFarlane into the house at about half-past nine and that she thought he left his stick in the hall. She soon went to bed and did not wake up until she heard people coming to the house because they had seen the fire. She says she thinks that the pieces of cloth come from the clothes that Mr Oldacre was wearing that night. That is all she told me but I am sure she is hiding something. I feel it."

Next, Holmes told me that Oldacre had been paying money to a "Mr Cornelius". This was the reason that he had so little money at the bank himself. Nobody could tell Holmes who Cornelius was. Holmes's face became very serious as he finished speaking. "I am afraid that Lestrade will be able to hang Mr McFarlane and I don't know how to stop him."

I went to bed soon after this but I don't think Holmes slept all night.

Chapter 5

When I got up next morning Sherlock Holmes was reading the morning newspapers. There was a letter from Norwood on the table. It said:

Come to Norwood soon. I have discovered a new fact. I am sure now that McFarlane killed Oldacre.
Lestrade.

"Lestrade is clearly very pleased because he thinks he has beaten me for the first time," said Holmes. "I must go to Norwood. Please, Watson, will you come with me? I need a friend today."

When we arrived at Oldacre's house, Lestrade was waiting for us. He looked very pleased with himself.

"Hello, Mr Holmes," he cried. "Have you found your man yet?"

"I haven't found anything yet," replied Holmes.

"Well, I have," said Lestrade.

"You certainly seem very pleased with yourself," Holmes answered.

Lestrade laughed loudly and said to me, "Sherlock Holmes really doesn't like being beaten, does he, Dr Watson?" I did not reply and he continued, "Please come this way, gentlemen."

He led us into the hall. "This is where McFarlane must have come to get his hat after he killed Oldacre," he said. "Now look here."

He pointed to a mark on the wall. It was the mark of a

29

Holmes and Watson drive a carriage to Norwood

finger and it was the colour of blood.

"That is the mark of John Hector McFarlane's finger," said Lestrade. He showed us a piece of paper. On it there was another mark exactly the same as the one on the wall. Mr McFarlane had made it in prison that morning.

"That is the end of the case," said Lestrade proudly.

"Yes, it is," I agreed.

"Yes, it *is*," said Holmes in a strange voice. I looked at him; I was surprised to see that he looked very happy. Lestrade continued to talk in a very proud way. He thought Holmes was beaten, but I could see that Holmes was really laughing at him.

"Very good!" said Holmes. "This must be a lesson to us all, mustn't it, Lestrade?"

"Yes, it must," the detective replied.

"Who discovered this mark?" asked Holmes.

"Mr Oldacre's servant, the old woman. She found it this morning."

"You are sure that the mark was there yesterday?" said Holmes.

Lestrade thought that my friend was mad, and I must say that I could not understand what he meant by his question.

"Mr Holmes," said Lestrade, "how do you think that McFarlane could get out of prison to come here and make the mark? Even if it were possible it would be a stupid thing to do."

Then Holmes said, "Well, it is the mark of his finger, we can be sure of that."

"Yes, we certainly can," said Lestrade. "And now, gentlemen, I must go. I am a busy man and I must write my report on this case." He left us and went quickly into the sitting room.

When he had closed the door I asked Holmes why he had looked so pleased when Lestrade showed us the mark.

"Because I *know* that it wasn't there yesterday. I looked at the wall carefully. The police didn't look as carefully as I did; that is why they are not the best detectives. Now, Watson, let's go for a walk in the garden."

I followed Holmes. I couldn't understand how the mark had got there and I could see that Holmes wasn't going to tell me yet. He looked at every part of the outside of the house, then we went back inside and he carefully looked in every room. We looked in every cupboard and walked down every passage. We were in the last passage at the top of the house when Holmes suddenly started laughing.

"This is an interesting case, Watson," he said. "Lestrade thinks he has beaten me; he had fun when we were talking about the mark in the hall, but I think I can have some fun now. What shall I do ...? I know!"

We went down to the room where Lestrade was working and Holmes asked, "Are you writing your report, Mr Lestrade?"

"Of course I am," the detective replied. He sounded rather angry with us for coming in when he was busy.

"Isn't it too early to write a report?" Holmes asked. Lestrade put down his pen and looked at him. He knew Holmes well and he could see that he had something important to tell him.

"What do you mean?" he asked.

"Well, there is one important person in this case that you haven't spoken to," said Holmes.

"Really? Who? Can you show me this person?" said Lestrade in a very surprised voice.

"Yes, I think I can," said Holmes, "but I shall need some help. How many policemen are there here?"

"Three," said Lestrade.

"Are they strong men, with good loud voices?" asked Holmes.

"Yes, they are, but I don't see how their voices can help us."

"You'll soon see," said Holmes. "Now, please ask one policeman to bring some old newspapers. There are a lot in the hall. The other two must bring buckets of water."

The policemen brought the things and all six of us went up to the top of the house. The policemen were smiling and Lestrade still thought that Holmes was mad. I did not know what my friend was going to do.

Chapter 6

Sherlock Holmes walked to the end of the passage and carefully put the newspapers on the floor. Then he said to me, "Watson, please open the window, then set fire to these papers."

I did what he asked and the papers soon started to burn. Next Holmes said, "Now I want you all to shout, 'Fire!' with me as loudly as you can. One, two, three——"

"Fire!" we all shouted.

"Again!" cried Holmes.

"FIRE!"

"Again!"

"FIRE!" we shouted very loudly indeed.

Suddenly the wall at the end of the passage opened just like a door. An ugly little man ran out, like a rabbit coming out of its hole.

"Very good," said Holmes. "Watson, put some water on the fire!" Then he said to Lestrade, "This is Mr Jonas Oldacre."

Lestrade couldn't believe it at first. He said, "Where

have you been for the last two days?"

Oldacre laughed, but he was clearly afraid of Lestrade. "I haven't hurt anyone," he said.

"You haven't hurt anyone!" repeated Lestrade angrily. "Because of you Mr Hector McFarlane is in prison. We thought he had killed you. He was in danger of being hanged."

"I only did it for a joke," said Oldacre.

"You aren't going to play any more jokes now!" said Lestrade. He told the policemen to take Oldacre away.

When they had gone, Lestrade said, "I must thank you, Mr Holmes. I was rude to you earlier today and I am sorry. I really thought that the case was finished. It would have been very bad indeed if Mr McFarlane had been hanged for something he didn't do."

"Don't worry," said Holmes kindly. "Nobody will know what happened. You can change your report and it isn't necessary to say that I did anything to help."

"But don't you want people to know how clever you have been?" asked Lestrade.

"No," said Holmes. "I am happy with my work and that is enough for me. Now, let's see where that rat has been living."

The end of the passage had been made into a small room. Inside it there was a little furniture. On the table there was some food and water and also some papers. When the door was closed it was impossible to see that the room was there.

"Oldacre was a builder, so he was easily able to make this place for himself," said Holmes. "He didn't need anyone to help him with his plan except his servant."

"How did you know that he was here?" asked Lestrade.

"I thought he must be hiding somewhere in the house,"

Holmes replied. "I found that this passage was shorter than the one underneath it; then it was clear to me where he was."

"That was clever," said Lestrade, "but what made you think that he was in the house?"

"The finger mark," said Holmes. "I knew that it was not there yesterday because I looked; so it must have been put there last night."

"But McFarlane was in prison. How was it done?"

"I think you will find that when Oldacre and McFarlane were working on the papers they used a lot of red wax to close the envelopes," said Holmes. "I think Oldacre asked McFarlane to put his finger on the wax to make sure that the envelopes closed properly. That would make a clear mark on the wax. Later Oldacre used some more wax to put the mark on the wall. He probably used a little blood from his own finger."

"Wonderful!" said Lestrade. "Wonderful! But why did he do all these things, Mr Holmes?"

I wanted to laugh when I saw this detective, who had been so proud in the morning, asking questions like a child talking to his teacher.

"That doesn't seem difficult," said Sherlock Holmes. "Oldacre hated McFarlane's mother because she once refused to marry him ... You didn't know that, Lestrade, because you never visited Blackheath. Oldacre is a very nasty and dangerous man. He waited for many years for a chance to make Mrs McFarlane unhappy. He wanted to make the police hang her son and at the same time he wanted to get some money."

"Get some money, how?" asked Lestrade.

"The papers we looked at show that Oldacre had troubles with his money." said Holmes. "I think he wanted to disappear and escape from the people he owed money to. He paid a lot of money to this 'Mr Cornelius' but I don't think that there is a man with that name. I think Oldacre was going to change his own name to Cornelius after he disappeared.

"The will gave Mr McFarlane a reason for killing him and the fire meant that there was no need for a dead body. After a time people would forget Jonas Oldacre. Mr Cornelius, of course, would live in a different part of England – or in another country. It was the clever plan of a nasty man. But now, Mr Lestrade, let's go and ask him one or two more questions."

We went down to the room where the policemen were keeping Jonas Oldacre. When he saw us he said once again, "I only did it for a joke. I didn't want to hurt dear Mr McFarlane."

"I don't think anyone will believe that," said Lestrade. "I think you will have to go to prison, Mr Oldacre."

"And I think the police will take all Mr Cornelius's money too," Holmes added.

Oldacre looked at Holmes and said in a very angry voice, "I will kill you, Sherlock Holmes!"

Holmes smiled and said, "You are not the first man who has said that to me, but I think that you are going to be too busy in prison to do anything for the next few years. Before you go, I have a question for you. What did you burn with the wood to make the police doctor think that a human body might have been burnt? Was it a dead dog, or perhaps some rabbits?"

Oldacre sat still in angry silence. Holmes laughed and said, "He doesn't want to tell us, Watson. Well, it isn't important. If you ever write the story of the Norwood builder you can say that it was rabbits."

The Golden Glasses

Chapter 1

It was a very stormy night near the end of November. Sherlock Holmes and I were reading by the fire. Outside we could hear only the sound of the wind and the rain. It was late, and most people were in bed.

Holmes put down his book, and said, "I'm glad that we don't have to go out tonight, Watson."

"So am I," I replied.

Just then we heard a carriage stop outside the house. Someone was getting out. I went to the window and looked out into the darkness.

"Someone is coming here," I said.

"I wonder who it is," Holmes answered.

Very soon we knew who our visitor was. It was Stanley Hopkins, a young detective from Scotland Yard. Holmes and I had helped him with a few cases in the past.

"Come in, and sit down by the fire," said Holmes. "It's a very cold, wet night. I think you must have an interesting case for me!"

"Yes, I have," the detective replied. "Have you seen the newspapers this evening, Mr Holmes?"

"No," said Holmes. "I have been busy with a book."

Hopkins said, "It doesn't matter. There were only a few facts in the newspapers. The case is very new; the police at Yoxley only sent for me this afternoon."

"Where is Yoxley?" I asked.

"It's in Kent," he replied. "It's a very small place. When

I arrived there, I thought this was going to be an easy case. Now it seems very difficult. A man is dead, and I really don't know why anyone wanted to kill him."

"Tell me everything," said Sherlock Holmes.

"Yoxley Old Place is a large house in the country near to a small village," said the detective. "About ten years ago an old man, Professor Coram, came to live there. He was sick, and he could only walk with a stick. After a few months his neighbours became friendly with him, but they did not visit his house often. People say that he is very clever. He spends most of his time working with his books. He has two servants and a gardener. The servants' names are Mrs Marker – she is his cook – and Susan Tarleton. They are good servants, and have been with him for quite a long time.

"The professor has been writing a book. About a year ago he decided that he needed a secretary to help him. A man came, but he wasn't very good, and he didn't stay with him very long. The second man who came was called Smith. He became a good friend and helper to the professor. They worked together every day, and the book is nearly finished. But now the young man is dead, and I think someone killed him.

"As I said before, very few people visit the house. The people in the house don't go out very often either. Old Mortimer, the gardener, has a cottage in the garden.

"Yoxley Old Place is near to the London road, and it is easy to open the garden gate. Someone could easily come to the house, get in, and escape quite quickly.

"I spoke to Susan Tarleton, the servant girl. She told me that she was working in one of the bedrooms between eleven and twelve o'clock this morning. Professor Coram was still in bed; he often gets up late. Smith was in his

Holmes and Watson at home at Baker Street

bedroom reading a book. After a few minutes she heard him go down to the room where he usually worked with the professor. Suddenly she heard a very loud cry. She ran down to the room, and found Mr Smith lying on the floor. He was nearly dead. There was a wound in his neck, and a lot of blood on the floor.

"Mr Smith managed to say a few words before he died. His voice was not strong, but Susan Tarleton thinks that he said 'The professor, it was she ...'

"I spoke to the cook next, but she arrived in the room after Mr Smith had died. The two women quickly went to the professor's bedroom. He was still in bed. He was frightened because he had heard the loud cry. He could not get out of bed without someone to help him. He cannot think of any reason why Mr Smith was killed.

"Mortimer got the police, and they sent for me. When I arrived I saw that everyone had been careful not to walk on the garden path. Nothing in the house had been moved either.

"I think someone very clever came to the house this morning. There were no marks on the garden path, but I could see that someone had walked along the grass beside the path. That person didn't want anyone to know that he or she had been there.

"I went to the room and looked at Mr Smith's body. There was a small knife on the floor, and I think that it killed him. It is the professor's and he always kept it on the table in that room. The wound was on the side of Smith's neck, near to the back. I don't think he made it himself."

"Perhaps he fell on the knife," said Holmes.

"No," replied the detective. "It was on the floor, but it was not near to the body. Oh, and the most important thing we found was this."

He gave Holmes a pair of glasses. Holmes took them and looked at them very carefully. After a few minutes he took a piece of paper and wrote something on it. Then he gave it to Stanley Hopkins. Hopkins read the note.

Try to find a woman who has plenty of money. She will be wearing good clothes. She has a thick nose, and her eyes are close together. She stares when she looks at things. She has visited an optician at least twice during the last two months. Her glasses are unusually strong, and rather expensive. There are not many good opticians in London, so I think you can find her easily.

The detective was surprised when he read this, and so was I. Holmes looked at our faces and laughed. He said, "Glasses can tell us many things about the people they belong to. These glasses must belong to a woman; they are very pretty. Mr Smith said 'it was she' before he died, and that too makes me think a woman was there. She must have money and like good things because the glasses are made of gold. Expensive glasses are always made to fit a person exactly. Watson, your nose is quite thick, but I am sure these are too big for you. My face is narrow, my eyes are close together, but it is difficult for me to look through the glasses. That is how I knew about her nose and eyes."

"But what about her staring, and the visits to the optician?" I asked.

Holmes replied, "People with bad eyes always stare when they look at things because they can't see easily. It was clear to me that the glasses had been mended twice, and I could see that the two places had been mended at different times. The gold is very new and yellow in one place; in the other it is a little older."

Hopkins said, "You are always so clever, Mr Holmes. I

think you know more about this case than I do now, and you have never been to Yoxley Old Place! Will you and Dr Watson come there with me tomorrow?"

We both said yes. We had to catch the train at six o'clock next day so Holmes asked Stanley Hopkins to stay with us for the night.

Chapter 2

The next day the weather was better, but it was still very cold. We took the train to a small town near Chatham. We had breakfast there, then we went by carriage to Yoxley Old Place. A policeman was waiting for us at the garden gate. Stanley Hopkins asked him if anything had happened in the night, but he said no. The police had found nothing new.

Hopkins said to Holmes, "Here is the garden path, Mr Holmes. You can see that there are no marks on it."

"Which side were the marks on the grass?" asked Holmes.

"This side," said the detective. He pointed at one side of the path.

"The grass is very narrow here," said Holmes. "But I can still see that someone has walked here. Is this the only way to get from the road to the house?"

"Yes," said Stanley Hopkins. "I am sure it is."

"So the lady must have come back this way too?"

"Yes."

"That was very clever of her," said Holmes. "She had to walk very carefully, I am sure. Well, I have seen all I want to see in the garden. Let's go into the house. I suppose the door to the garden is always open, so it was easy for her to get in," Holmes continued. "I don't think that she knew she was going to kill anyone, because she didn't bring a

Holmes and Watson take the train to Yoxley Old Place

knife or a gun. She used the professor's knife from the table."

We went into the house and Holmes said, "She came down this passage, but she didn't make any marks on the floor. Then she came into this room. How long was she here? Do you know?"

"She was only here for a few minutes, Mr Holmes," replied Hopkins. "The cook says that she was cleaning in here only a quarter of an hour before Mr Smith was killed. I forgot to tell you that yesterday."

Holmes said, "Good, so she was not here for longer than fifteen minutes. She went to that cupboard by the table. It is the only piece of furniture in here with a lock on it. If there is anything important in the room it must be in there."

He bent down and looked at the door of the cupboard. Then he stood up, and said, "Look!" He pointed at the door. "There is a small mark on the brass lock by the keyhole. Why didn't you tell me about this, Hopkins?"

"I didn't think it was important," said the detective. "There are always marks by keyholes."

"I know," said Holmes. "But this mark is very new. I think it was made only yesterday. Is Mrs Marker here?"

"Yes," said Hopkins. "Here she is."

Holmes asked Mrs Marker, "Did you see this mark when you cleaned the room yesterday?"

"No, I didn't."

"I'm sure you didn't," said Holmes. "I think that the person who killed Mr Smith made it. Who has the key to this lock?"

"The professor has it," Mrs Marker told Holmes. "He keeps it in his room with him."

Holmes's next question was, "Is it a simple key?"

The servant said, "No. That is a strong lock. The key is not a simple one."

Holmes told Mrs Marker she could go, and she left the room. Then he said to us, "Now we know what happened. The lady came into this room. She went to the cupboard, and tried to open it. Smith came in while she was doing that. She quickly tried to take the key out of the lock. She made that mark because she was in a hurry. Smith went to her, and she picked up the knife. He held her, so she struck him with the knife. She wanted to get away. He fell to the floor, and she ran out of the room. But she had lost her glasses.

"There are two passages outside. One goes to the back door, the other goes to the professor's room, doesn't it?"

"Yes," said Hopkins. "There is no way out of the house by the second passage."

"Let's go and see the professor now," said Holmes.

We went down the passage to the professor's room. Holmes looked at the walls and floor of the passage, and said, "Do you notice anything strange about this passage, Inspector?"

"No," said Stanley Hopkins. "Nothing. It is just like the other one."

"That is what I mean," said Holmes. "The walls and floor are exactly the same colours as in the other passage."

"Is that important?" asked the detective.

"I think it may be," replied Holmes. "But I am not sure about that yet."

Chapter 3

We went into the professor's room. It was a very large room, and the walls were covered with books. There were so many books that some of them were lying on the floor in front of the shelves. The professor's bed was in the middle, and the professor was lying in it. He had white hair. He had a big white beard too, but near to his mouth it was dirty and yellow. He was smoking a cigarette. The room smelt of cigarette smoke, and there were many boxes of cigarettes on the table. When I looked at the professor's hand, I saw that it was yellow from the cigarettes, just like his beard.

He said hello to Holmes, then he said, "Do you smoke, Mr Holmes? These are very good cigarettes; I smoke a lot of them. Smoking is one of the few things that makes me happy. I can't walk easily, so I can't go out. I only have my work and my cigarettes. Now that Smith is dead I can't even work. He was a good young man; he helped me very much. I am sorry about what has happened to him, very sorry."

Holmes took a cigarette and lit it. He walked round the room while he was smoking. The professor continued talking.

"I'm happy that you've come, Mr Holmes. I'm sure that you will be able to help us."

I noticed that Holmes was smoking quickly – much more quickly than he usually did. He had already smoked four cigarettes when the professor stopped talking.

He said to the professor, "I know that you were in bed when Smith was killed, so you don't know anything about it. But can you tell me what his last words meant? 'The professor, it was she . . .'."

"No, I can't," said the professor. "But Susan Tarleton is only a girl. Perhaps she didn't listen carefully to what he said. I'm sure he didn't speak clearly – remember, he was dying!"

"Can you think of any reason for his death?" was

Holmes's next question.

"Well, Mr Holmes," said the professor. "I will say this only to you and to nobody else, because it's not a nice thing to say. I don't want other people to think badly of Mr Smith, but I think he killed himself. I think he was in love. He had some glasses belonging to a woman. Perhaps he loved her very much, but she didn't love him. People sometimes kill themselves for that reason."

Holmes looked surprised when he heard that idea. It made him think. He walked up and down the room silently. At last he spoke to the professor.

"What's in the cupboard in the room where Smith died?"

The professor replied, "Nothing important to a thief, Mr Holmes. Just papers and letters from my poor wife. She is dead now. You can look in the cupboard if you want to. Here is the key."

Holmes took the key and looked at it. Then he said, "No, I don't think I need to look in the cupboard. You may be right about Smith, Professor Coram. I will think about your idea. I may have an answer for you after I have had something to eat. I will come to you then, but I won't come before two o'clock. I am sure that you need to rest."

The professor looked pleased when Holmes said this, and said, "Yes, I am tired. Please don't come here until two o'clock. I want to be alone."

Holmes and I walked in the garden. Holmes did not seem very happy, he didn't seem interested in the case now. I asked him, "Do you think you can find the answer now, Holmes?"

"I'm not sure," he replied. "But those cigarettes I smoked may help us."

"Really? How?"

"You will see later," he said. "Now, here comes Mrs Marker. I'll talk to her for five minutes." He began talking to the cook. "I suppose the professor doesn't eat very much," he said. "People who smoke too much usually eat too little."

"Sometimes he eats a lot, sometimes a little," said Mrs Marker.

"And today?" Holmes asked. "I saw him smoke so many cigarettes that I'm sure he didn't want any breakfast."

"You're wrong, sir!" the cook replied. "He had a large breakfast, and he's asked for another large meal already. I'm surprised; when I knew that poor Mr Smith was dead I didn't want anything to eat. The professor is a strange man."

After this Holmes did not talk very much. He seemed interested in nothing. The only person he listened to was Susan, the servant. She told him that Mr Smith had been out to the village in the morning, not long before he was killed.

At two o'clock Holmes said, "It's time for us to go and see the professor again, gentlemen."

Chapter 4

The old man had just finished eating. His plate was clean, he had eaten everything. He was sitting on a chair, and he was already smoking another cigarette.

"Well, Mr Holmes," he said. "Have you found an answer to this case?"

He pushed his box of cigarettes towards Holmes. Holmes put out his hand to take one, but he knocked the box off the table and all the cigarettes fell on the floor. Holmes, Stanley Hopkins and I got down on the floor to pick them up. When we had finished, Holmes stood up, and said to Professor Coram, "Yes, I have the answer!"

"Really?" said Professor Coram. "Where did you find it? In the garden?" His face was angry as he spoke to Holmes.

"No," said my friend. "The answer is here in your room!"

"And when did you find this answer?"

"Two minutes ago," said Holmes.

Then the professor said, "I am sure you are not being serious, Mr Holmes. This is an important case; Smith is dead. Please don't be funny."

"I'm *not* being funny," said Holmes. "I *am* sure about what I know. I don't know everything yet, but I know that you have done something bad. I will tell you what I think.

"Yesterday, a lady came into your house and went into the room with the cupboard. She had brought her own key, and she was going to open the cupboard. It was a new key with a sharp point and it made a mark on the brass lock of the door. There is no sharp point on your key; I noticed that when you gave it to me this morning. I know she did not use your key, so I think that you did not know that she had come into the house. She came here as a thief to steal something from the cupboard."

"This is all very interesting," said Coram. "But can't you tell us more? What happened to this lady after that?"

"I will try to tell you," replied Holmes. "Your secretary came into the room and found her there. She killed him, but I think it was a mistake. If she had wanted to kill someone she would have brought her own knife.

"She lost her glasses in the fight, but she had to run away quickly. Her eyes were not good and she made a second mistake. She went down the wrong passage. It was an easy mistake to make, as they both have floors and walls of the same colour. She didn't go to the door, she came to your room, Professor."

"Do you mean that she came in here and I didn't even see her?" cried the professor. His face was white, and he seemed frightened.

"No, I mean that she came in here and you *did* see her!" said Holmes. "I think you knew who she was. You spoke to her and helped her."

The professor laughed loudly, "You are mad, Mr Holmes, mad! Where is this woman now?"

Holmes pointed at one of the walls. It was covered with bookshelves. "She is there!" he said.

We all looked at the shelves that he was pointing to. We saw nothing but books. Then the whole bookcase began to move. The wall was opening like a door. A woman came into the room. The professor cried out loudly.

She was covered with dirt and dust from behind the shelves. "Yes," she said in a strange voice. "I am here!"

Chapter 5

Hopkins went to the woman and said, "You must come with me."

"I won't try to escape," she replied. "I know that you know I killed Smith. I haven't got very much time, but I want to tell you the truth about this man."

She pointed at the professor. "He is not English; he is Russian. I will not tell you his name, it is not necessary."

Professor Coram looked a little happier when she said this. He replied, "Thank you, Anna, thank you."

She looked at him angrily, and continued. "Why do you want to live? Your life is nothing, you are an animal.

50

"Gentlemen, I am this man's wife. We used to live in a city in Russia. I will not tell you the name of that city."

Again the old man said, "Thank you, Anna."

"We were revolutionaries," she said. "We were fighting to make our country a better place. We had friends who were also revolutionaries. The police wanted to catch us. They wanted to send us to prison, or kill us.

"We decided to kill a policeman. We wanted to show people that we were strong. One day one of us really did kill a policeman. The police couldn't catch us, so they offered a lot of money to anyone who could tell them who had done it.

"My husband told the police the name of the killer. He got the money. All the other revolutionaries were caught. Some of us were killed, and some were sent to prison. I was lucky; I was only sent to prison for ten years.

"There was one young man called Alexis, another revolutionary. He didn't want us to kill the policeman. He tried to stop us; he wrote letters to me asking me to make the men change the plan. But my husband hid those letters. He wanted Alexis to die. Alexis was lucky; he didn't die, but he was sent to prison for a very long time. He is in prison now, and he will stay there for at least another twenty years."

She looked at the professor very angrily, and said, "Yes, he is in prison, and you are free. You beast!"

The woman's face was white. She looked weak and ill. "I must finish what I am saying quickly," she said. "I came out of prison last year, and I wanted to get the letters Alexis wrote to me. I knew that if the government in Russia saw them, they would know that Alexis had tried to stop us killing the policeman. Then they would let him out of prison.

"I came to England to find my husband. I didn't know where he was living. It took me a long time to find Yoxley Old Place. When I did find his new home I sent a man here. He was the first secretary, the man who worked here before Smith. He found out where the letters were kept, and he got a key for me. But he wouldn't help me any more, because he thought I wanted to kill my husband.

"So I had to come here myself. When I was coming to the house I met Mr Smith. I didn't know that he worked for my husband. I asked him where Professor Coram lived."

"Yes," said Holmes. "I think he came back here and told the professor that he had met you. That is why he said 'The professor, it was she . . .' before he died. He meant you – the woman he had been talking to that morning."

"You must let me speak," said the woman. Her face was even whiter than before. "I didn't want to kill Smith. I struck him with the knife because it was the only thing on the table. It was the first thing I saw. I ran out of the room, but I had lost my glasses. I made a mistake because I couldn't see. I came down the wrong passage. I came into this room.

"My husband was frightened and angry when he saw me. He said he would give me to the police. I knew that he couldn't do that. If he did, other revolutionaries would know where he was living. They would come here and kill him. I wanted to escape because of Alexis. My husband wanted me to escape because he was afraid of my revolutionary friends. He decided to keep me here in this room until the police had gone. There is a secret place behind the bookshelves that only he knew about. I stayed there for many hours. He took large meals so that he could give me food. He said that when the police had gone I could leave the house and he would say nothing."

She gave Holmes some papers, and said, "Please take these to the Russian Embassy in London ... Alexis will be let out of prison if you do ... These are my last words, Mr Holmes ... You ... you ... must help me!"

She fell to the ground. Quickly Holmes bent over her. He took a small bottle from her hand; it was empty. He said, "She is dead, Watson. She took poison before she came out from her hiding place."

Chapter 6

There were only a few more things for Holmes, Hopkins and me to do at Yoxley. Soon we were able to catch the train back to London. Holmes said to us, as we were travelling, "That was not really a difficult case, but the glasses were important. I couldn't have found the answer without them. It was clear to me that the woman's eyes were very weak, so when she had lost her glasses she couldn't see well.

"If she had escaped from the house she would have made marks on the path. She couldn't run along the grass by the path without her glasses. The grass is very narrow; she would have fallen, or put her feet on the path. So I thought that she had never left the house.

"It was the first time she had been in the house, and she made a mistake. The two passages are nearly the same, and she went down the wrong one. There is no door from the professor's room to the garden.

"'Perhaps she's still in the professor's room,' I thought. 'But where?'

"I looked at the floor, but it was very strong. I didn't think that there could be any secret places under it. Then I looked at the bookshelves. You can often find a secret place behind them in old houses. There were books on the

53

floor in front of most of the shelves, but not in one place. I thought that the shelves there might open like a door.

"I smoked a lot of cigarettes and I let the ash fall on the floor in front of those shelves. When the woman came out to eat her food, her feet made marks in the ash.

"When we came back to the room I knocked the box of cigarettes on the floor. I wanted to get down and look carefully at my ash. When I saw the marks in it, I was sure that she was there."

Our train was now arriving in London.

"Well, Hopkins," said Holmes. "Here we are at Charing Cross Station. I know you must go to Scotland Yard, but Watson and I must go to another place. We have some papers, and we must take them to the Russian Embassy."

Questions

Questions on each story

The number in brackets after each question shows you which chapter to look at.

The Six Napoleons
1 What had somebody been breaking? (1)
2 Where were Dr Barnicott's busts? (1)
3 Where was the dead man? (2)
4 What had happened to Mr Harker's bust? (2)
5 Why didn't the murderer break the bust at the nearest empty house? (Because . . .) (3)
6 What did Holmes want to keep? (3)
7 Whose photograph did Holmes show to Morse Hudson? (4)
8 Why did the police arrest Beppo? (4)
9 Who had bought the other two busts from Harding Brothers? (4)
10 Who was the dead man? (5)
11 Where did Holmes expect to find Beppo? (5)
12 What did the man do when he left the house? (6)
13 Whose house was it? (6)
14 What did Mr Sandeford bring? (7)
15 How much did Holmes pay Sandeford? (7)
16 What did Holmes do to the bust? (8)
17 What was inside the bust? (8)
18 What did Lestrade invite Holmes to do? (8)

The Norwood Builder
1 What was Hector McFarlane's work? (1)
2 What did the police think McFarlane had done? (1)
3 Where had McFarlane spent the night? (1)
4 Whose name was in Oldacre's will to get all his money? (2)
5 What did Oldacre ask McFarlane not to do? (2)
6 Where did Holmes want to go first? (2)
7 When did Oldacre write his will? (3)

8 When did he write the parts that were hard to read? (3)
9 Why did McFarlane's mother refuse to marry Oldacre? (4)
10 Why did Oldacre have only a little money in his bank? (4)
11 Where, in the hall, was the finger mark? (5)
12 Who found the finger mark? (5)
13 What did the policemen take to the top of the house? (5)
14 Where did Oldacre appear from? (6)
15 What did Holmes notice about the passages? (6)
16 Who was going to be "Mr Cornelius"? (6)
17 What did Oldacre burn with the wood? (6)

The Golden Glasses
1 Who was the visitor? (1)
2 Where had he been? (1)
3 Who was dead? (1)
4 How did Holmes know so much about the woman? (1)
5 What did Holmes see on the cupboard lock? (2)
6 Who had the key? (2)
7 What was strange about the passage to the professor's room? (2)
8 What was the smell in the professor's room? (3)
9 What did the professor say about the cause of Smith's death? (3)
10 What did Mrs Marker say about the professor's meals? (3)
11 At what time did they go back to the professor's room? (3)
12 What made the mark on the cupboard lock? (4)
13 Why did Holmes think that killing Smith was a mistake? (4)
14 Why did the bookcase move? (4)
15 In Russia, what were Anna and her husband? (5)
16 What did Alexis try to do? (5)
17 Who found out where the letters from Alexis were? (5)
18 What did Anna ask Holmes to do? (5)
19 Why did Holmes drop ash on the floor? (6)
20 Why did he knock the box of cigarettes on the floor? (6)

Questions on the whole book

These are harder questions. Read the Introduction, and think hard about the questions before you answer them. Some of the questions ask for your opinion, and there is no fixed answer.

1 Find these words, and then answer the questions.

The Six Napoleons

a "Those busts! Can't you forget them, Mr Holmes? They are not important."
   1 Whose words are these?
   2 What, in the speaker's mind, *is* "important"?
   3 Do you think the speaker was right? Can you give a reason?

b "We were lucky the pearl was not in Mr Harker's bust."
   1 Who said the words?
   2 What "pearl" is meant?
   3 Why were they "lucky"? (What would have happened if it had been in Harker's bust?)

The Norwood Builder

c "I can see that you're not married and that you're a lawyer."
   1 Who is the speaker?
   2 How does he know the two facts?
   3 What does the remark tell us about the speaker?

d "I only did it for a joke."
   1 Who is the speaker?
   2 What does "it" mean?
   3 Is the remark true? If not, what *is* the truth?

The Golden Glasses

e "But what about her staring, and the visits to the optician?"
   1 Who asks the question?
   2 Who is the person spoken about ("*her* staring")?
   3 What has been said about *staring* and the *optician*?
   4 Who answers the question, and how does he know the answer?

2 Lestrade, a detective from Scotland Yard, comes into two of the stories in this book. Which of these sentences (*a* or *b*) is true in your opinion? Give a reason or examples to support your answer.
   a Lestrade is a fool.
   b Lestrade seems foolish because Holmes's mind is so much sharper.

3 What did Sherlock Holmes learn or deduce from
   a old newspaper reports of May of the year before? (*The Six Napoleons*)
   b the writing on Oldacre's will? (*The Norwood Builder*)
   c marks on the cigarette ash he dropped? (*The Golden Glasses*)

New words

arrest
take (a person) to the police station because he or she has broken the law

ash
grey dusty matter that is left after something has been burnt

character
(1) a person in a story;
(2) the special nature of a particular person, causing him or her to behave in his or her own way

deduction
using known facts to work out (**deduce**) in one's mind the causes of those facts

handsome
good-looking (in a manly way)

joke
a funny story or an action to make us laugh

lawyer
a person who has studied law

method
a way of doing something

novel
a long story with invented

people and happenings, printed as a book

optician
a person who makes and mends eyeglasses

pearl
a white round jewel that grows in shellfish under the sea

plaster bust
the shape of the head and top part of the body (**hust**) of a person, made from a white matter (**plaster**) that is soft when wet but hard when it dries

revolutionary
a person who joins others to fight against the government of a country

secret society
a group of people who join together secretly

walking stick
a stick to help a person to walk

will
a paper that shows who you want your money to go to when you die